CW00670661

the seahorses

do it yourself

This publication is not authorised for sale in
the United States of America and / or Canada

Wise Publications

Guitar Tablature Explained

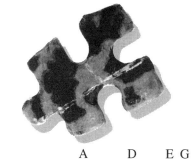

RHYTHM SLASHES are written above the stave. Strum chords in the rhythm indicated. Round noteheads indicate single notes.

THE MUSICAL STAVE shows pitches and rhythms and is divided by lines into bars. Pitches are named after the first seven letters of the alphabet.

TABLATURE graphically represents the guitar fingerboard. Each horizontal line represents a string, and each number represents a fret.

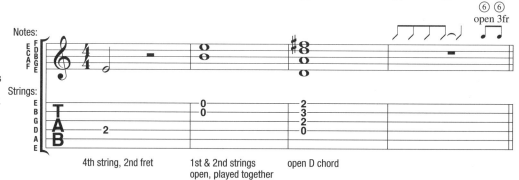

4th string, 2nd fret   1st & 2nd strings open, played together   open D chord

definitions for special guitar notation

SEMI-TONE BEND: Strike the note and bend up a semi-tone (1/2 step).

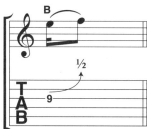

WHOLE-TONE BEND: Strike the note and bend up a whole-tone (whole step).

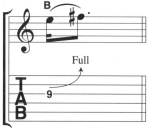

GRACE NOTE BEND: Strike the note and bend as indicated. Play the first note as quickly as possible.

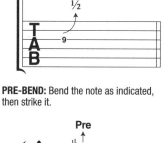

QUARTER-TONE BEND: Strike the note and bend up a 1/4 step.

BEND & RELEASE: Strike the note and bend up as indicated, then release back to the original note.

COMPOUND BEND & RELEASE: Strike the note and bend up and down in the rhythm indicated.

PRE-BEND: Bend the note as indicated, then strike it.

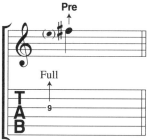

PRE-BEND & RELEASE: Bend the note as indicated. Strike it and release the note back to the original pitch.

UNISON BEND: Strike the two notes simultaneously and bend the lower note up to the pitch of the higher.

BEND & RESTRIKE: Strike the note and bend as indicated then restrike the string where the symbol occurs.

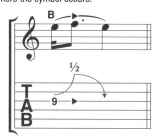

BEND, HOLD AND RELEASE: Same as bend and release but hold the bend for the duration of the tie.

BEND AND TAP: Bend the note as indicated and tap the higher fret while still holding the bend.

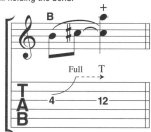

VIBRATO: The string is vibrated by rapidly bending and releasing the note with the fretting hand.

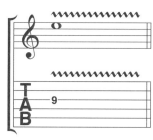

HAMMER-ON: Strike the first (lower) note with one finger, then sound the higher note (on the same string) with another finger by fretting it without picking.

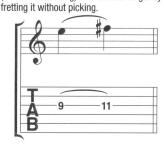

PULL-OFF: Place both fingers on the notes to be sounded, Strike the first note and without picking, pull the finger off to sound the second (lower) note.

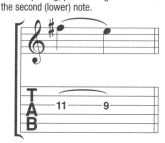

LEGATO SLIDE (GLISS): Strike the first note and then slide the same fret-hand finger up or down to the second note. The second note is not struck.

SHIFT SLIDE (GLISS & RESTRIKE): Same as legato slide, except the second note is struck.

TRILL: Very rapidly alternate between the notes indicated by continuously hammering on and pulling off.

TAPPING: Hammer ("tap") the fret indicated with the pick-hand index or middle finger and pull off to the note fretted by the fret hand.

PICK SCRAPE: The edge of the pick is rubbed down (or up) the string, producing a scratchy sound.

MUFFLED STRINGS: A percussive sound is produced by laying the fret hand across the string(s) without depressing, and striking them with the pick hand.

NATURAL HARMONIC: Strike the note while the fret-hand lightly touches the string directly over the fret indicated.

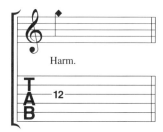

PINCH HARMONIC: The note is fretted normally and a harmonic is produced by adding the edge of the thumb or the tip of the index finger of the pick hand to the normal pick attack.

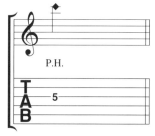

HARP HARMONIC: The note is fretted normally and a harmonic is produced by gently resting the pick hand's index finger directly above the indicated fret (in parentheses) while the pick hand's thumb or pick assists by plucking the appropriate string.

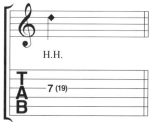

PALM MUTING: The note is partially muted by the pick hand lightly touching the string(s) just before the bridge.

RAKE: Drag the pick across the strings indicated with a single motion.

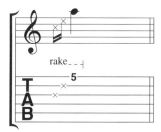

TREMOLO PICKING: The note is picked as rapidly and continuously as possible.

ARPEGGIATE: Play the notes of the chord indicated by quickly rolling them from bottom to top.

SWEEP PICKING: Rhythmic downstroke and/or upstroke motion across the strings.

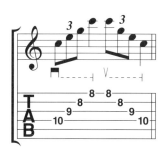

VIBRATO DIVE BAR AND RETURN: The pitch of the note or chord is dropped a specific number of steps (in rhythm) then returned to the original pitch.

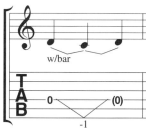

VIBRATO BAR SCOOP: Depress the bar just before striking the note, then quickly release the bar.

VIBRATO BAR DIP: Strike the note and then immediately drop a specific number of steps, then release back to the original pitch.

additional musical definitions

![accent]	(accent)	• Accentuate note (play it louder).
![accent]	(accent)	• Accentuate note with great intensity.
![staccato]	(staccato)	• Shorten time value of note.
![downstroke]		• Downstroke
V		• Upstroke

D.%. al Coda

D.C. al Fine

tacet

• Go back to the sign (%), then play until the bar marked *To Coda* ⊕ then skip to the section marked ⊕ *Coda*.

• Go back to the beginning of the song and play until the bar marked *Fine* (end).

• Instrument is silent (drops out).

• Repeat bars between signs.

1.	2.

• When a repeated section has different endings, play the first ending only the first time and the second ending only the second time.

NOTE: Tablature numbers in parentheses mean:
1. The note is sustained, but a new articulation (such as hammer on or slide) begins.
2. A note may be fretted but not necessarily played.

I WANT YOU TO KNOW

Words & Music by Chris Helme & Stuart Fletcher

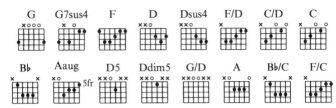

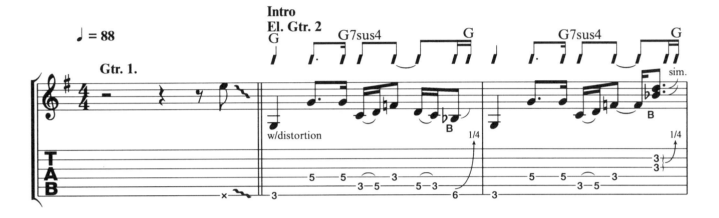

1. So did you 1.3. think that you had it all____ worked out____ but
(2.) all of your cards marked in ad - vance,__ as you

© Copyright 1997 PolyGram Music Publishing Limited, 47 British Grove, London W4.
All Rights Reserved. International Copyright Secured.

go out and   get load - ed, go and give it a   go,
sat down with   arms fold - ed, they don't wan - na know.
now you're feel - ing load - ed, you got no - where to   go,

let ring

1.

to Coda ⊕

I want you to know,

yeah I want you to know.

2. Were

P.M.

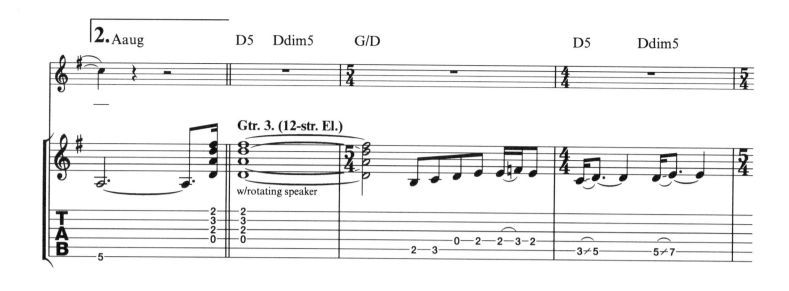

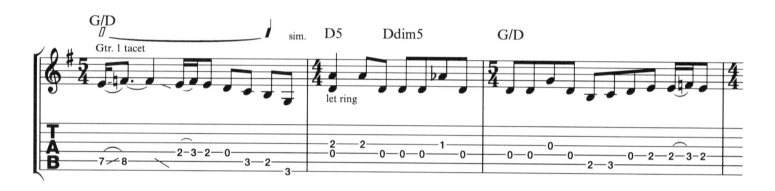

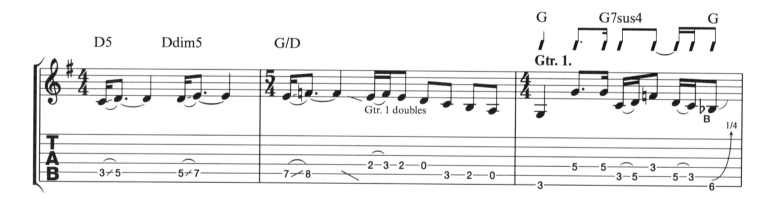

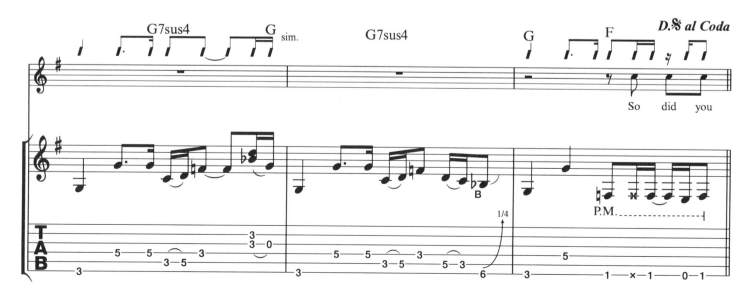

So did you

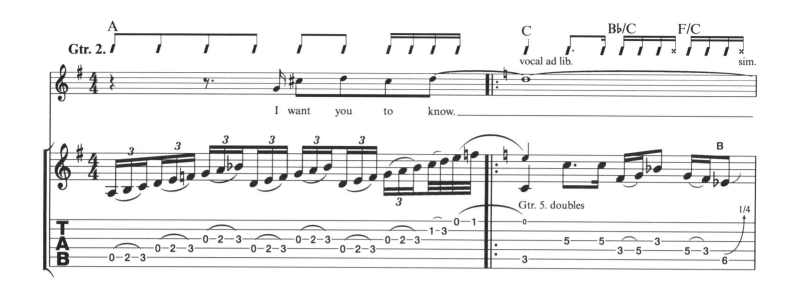

I want you to know.

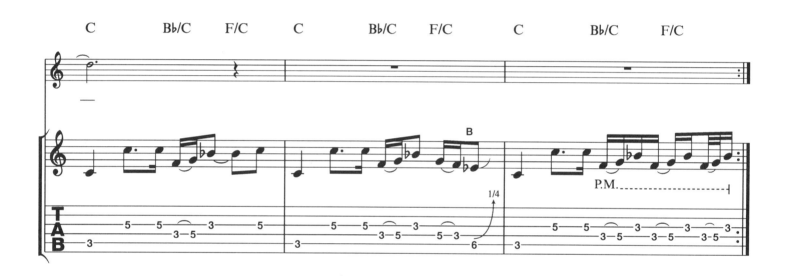

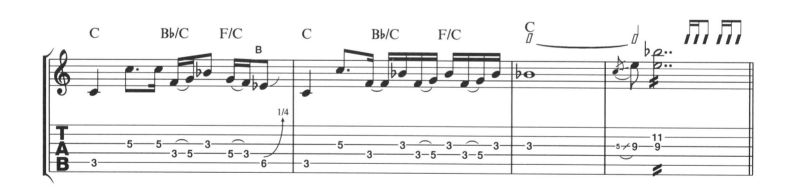

Outro

repeat to fade

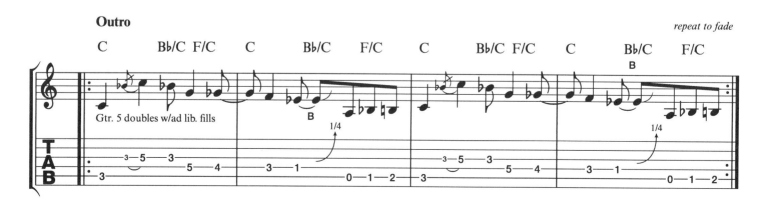

BLINDED BY THE SUN

Words & Music by Chris Helme

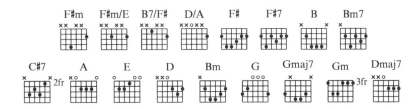

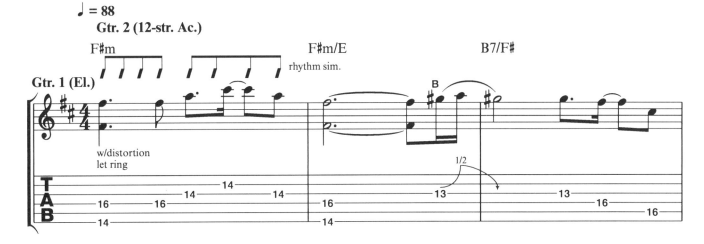

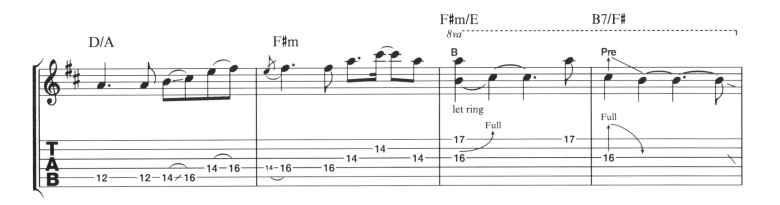

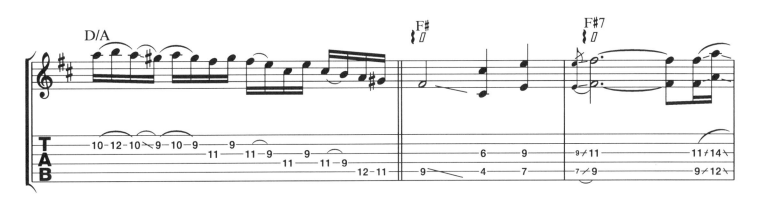

© Copyright 1997 PolyGram Music Publishing Limited, 47 British Grove, London W4.
All Rights Reserved. International Copyright Secured.

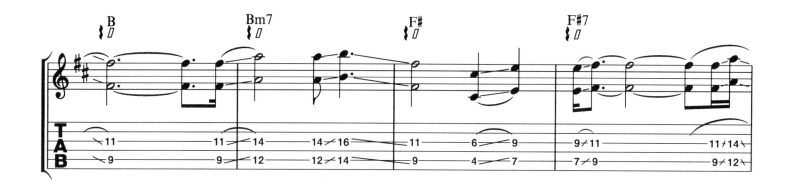

Verse

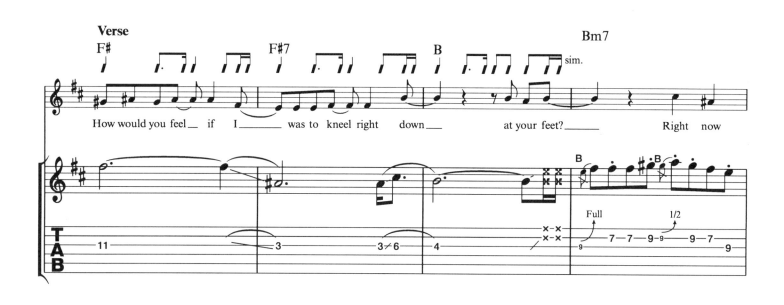

How would you feel__ if I_____ was to kneel right down__ at your feet?_____ Right now

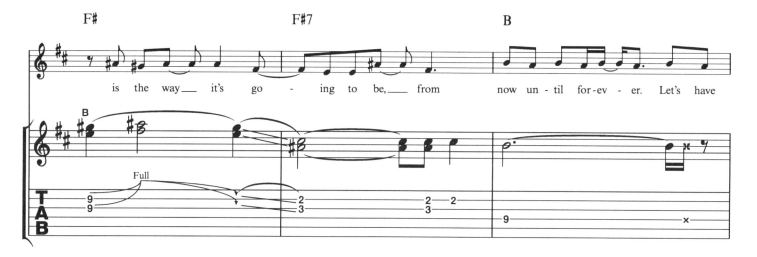

is the way__ it's go - ing to be,__ from now un - til for-ev - er. Let's have

less of get-ting cle-ver with_ me._____

Verse

Gtr. 3. tacet on repeat

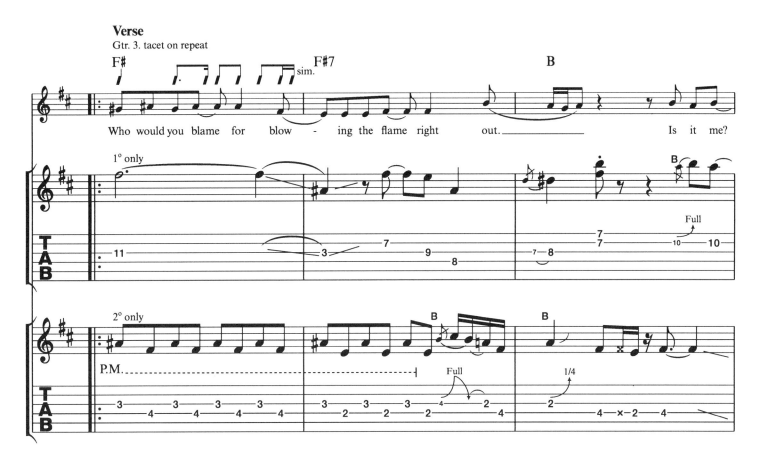

Who would you blame for blow - ing the flame right out._____ Is it me?

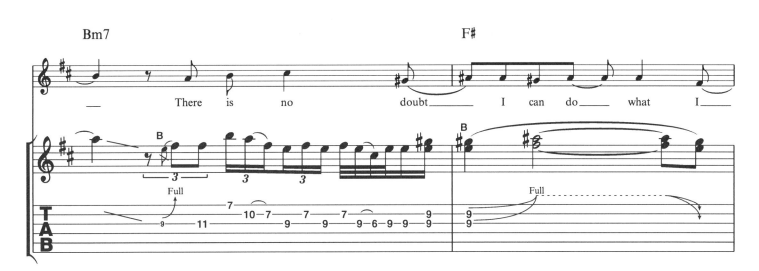

___ There is no doubt____ I can do____ what I___

SUICIDE DRIVE

Words & Music by John Squire

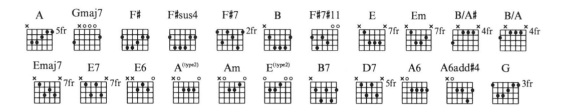

♩ = 152

Intro

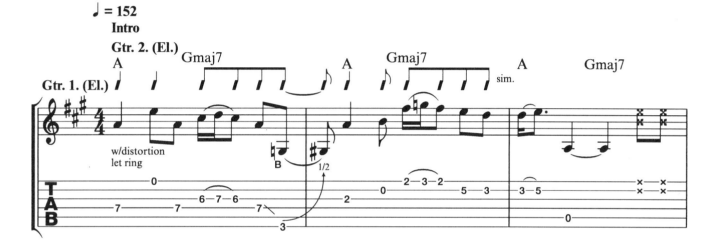

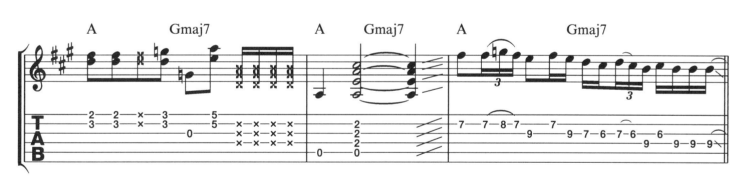

Verse

1. Please_____ may I leave the ta-
2. Drive_____ as fast as you can,___

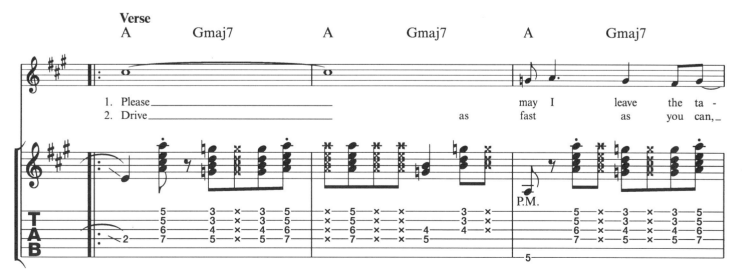

© Copyright 1997 PolyGram Music Publishing Limited, 47 British Grove, London W4.
All Rights Reserved. International Copyright Secured.

ride   I've   got a   place to go,   there's no - where to

hide   on Su - ic - ide   Drive.

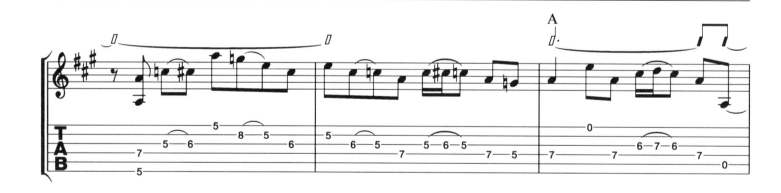

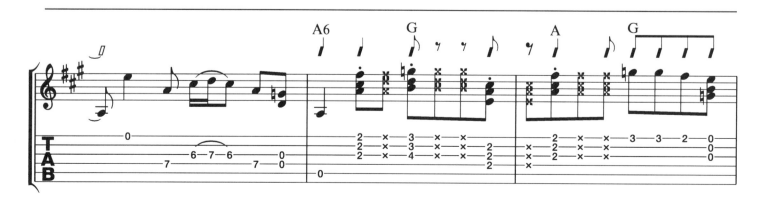

a tempo (♩ = 152)
Gtr. 2.

Sometimes this world just drives you crazy,___ lately___ yeah and the smoke gets in___ your___ eyes,___ run the exhaust back inside,___

let ring

THE BOY IN THE PICTURE

Words & Music by John Squire

© Copyright 1997 PolyGram Music Publishing Limited, 47 British Grove, London W4.
All Rights Reserved. International Copyright Secured.

just out of ___ reach, but ___ free. ___

Verse

And then the boy in the pic - ture he asked me ___

got a - ny tips, ___ where do I go wrong ___ and,

who am I going to be? ___

LOVE IS THE LAW

Words & Music by John Squire

© Copyright 1997 PolyGram Music Publishing Limited, 47 British Grove, London W4.
All Rights Reserved. International Copyright Secured.

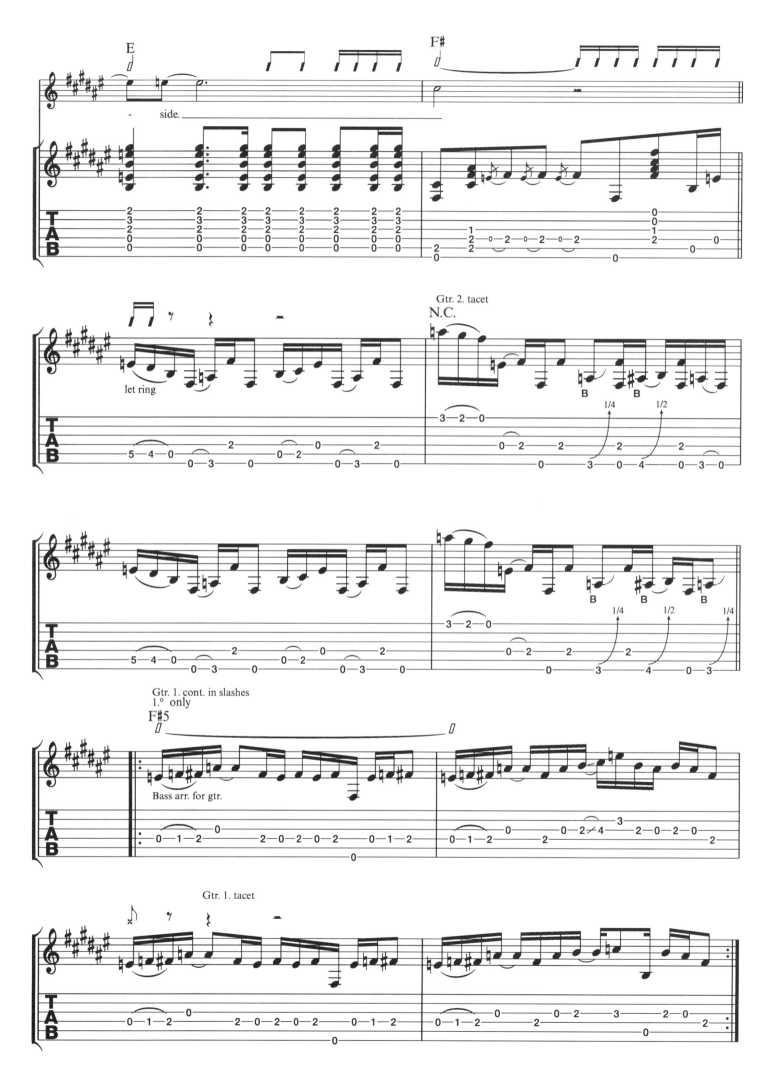

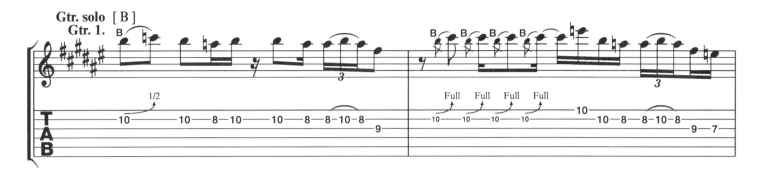

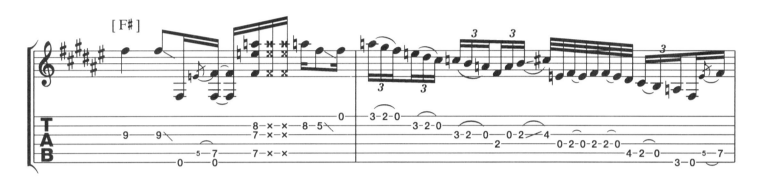

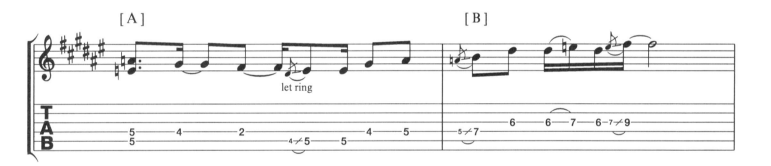

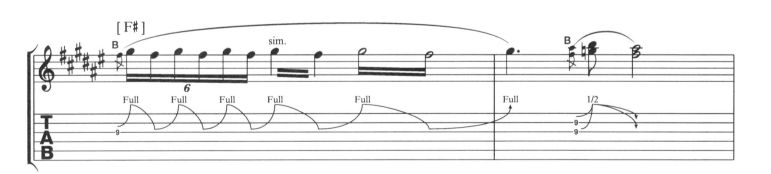

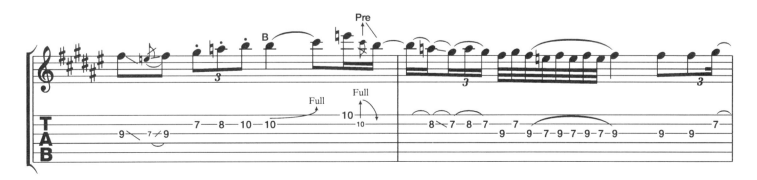

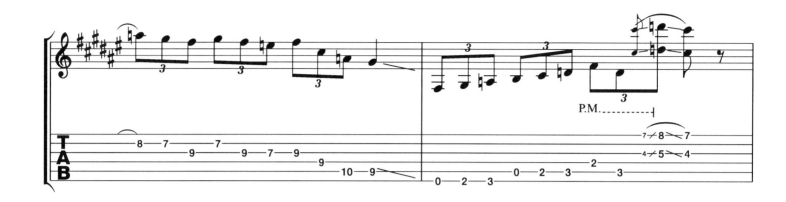

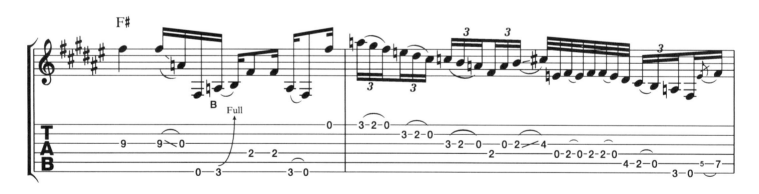

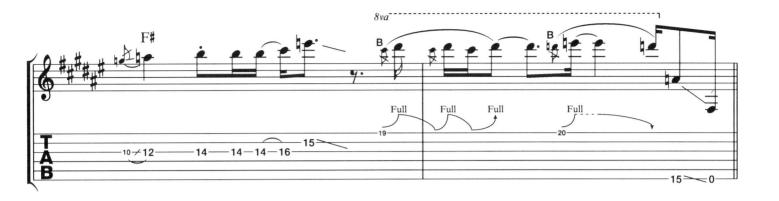

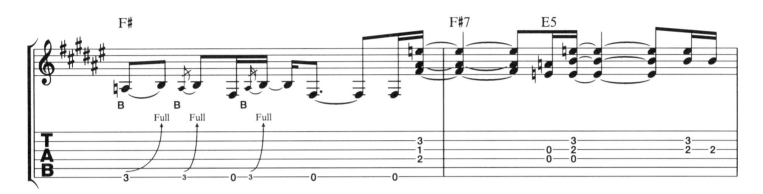

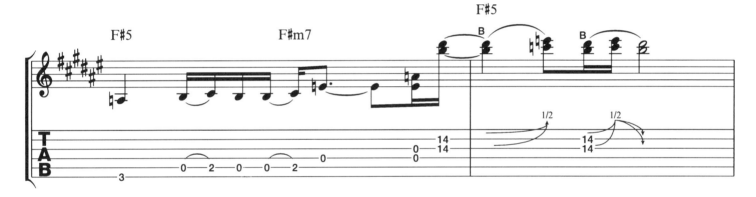

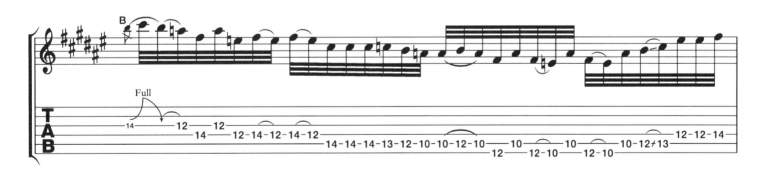

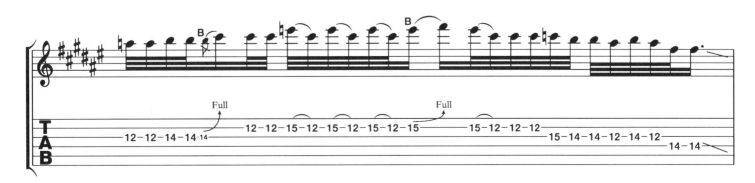

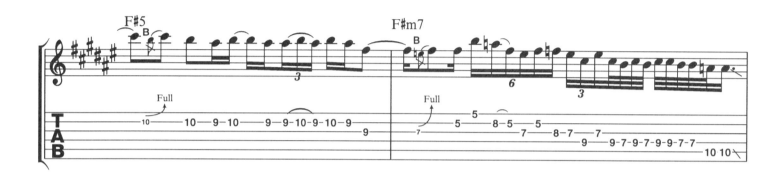

Gtr. 3. plays ad lib. w/effects

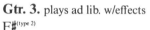

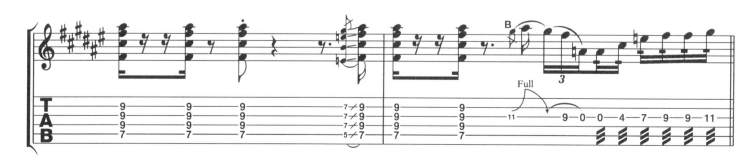

Gtr. 3. 2°ad lib.　F#5

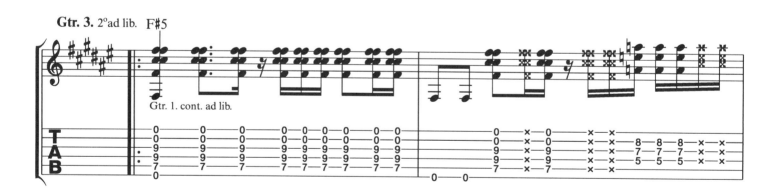

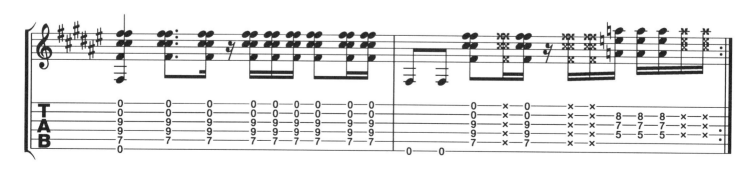

Verse 3:
Strap on Sally chased us down the alley,
We feared for our behinds
Oasis was a shop with shoes so hot,
They were sure to blow your minds
Running so fast I can taste the past,
Oh take me home

HAPPINESS IS EGGSHAPED

Words & Music by John Squire

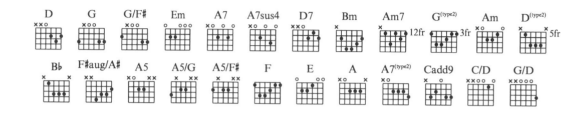

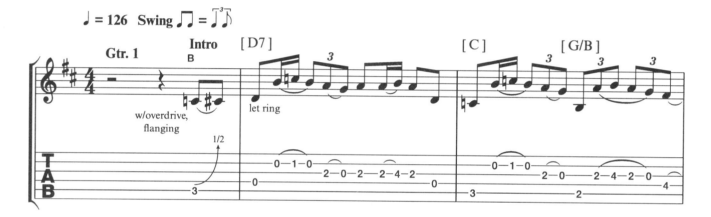

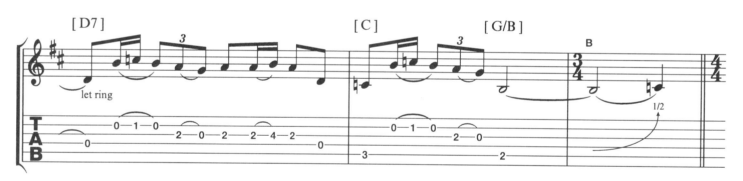

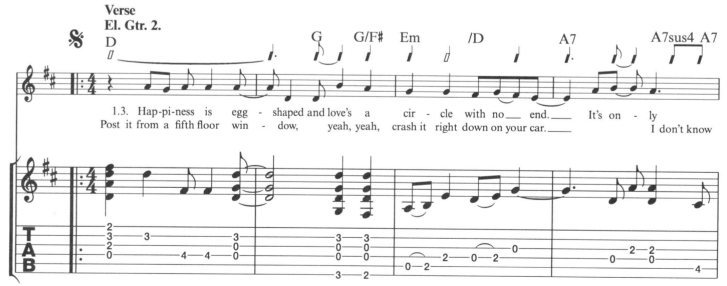

1.3. Hap-pi-ness is egg - shaped and love's a cir - cle with no___ end.___ It's on - ly
Post it from a fifth floor win - dow, yeah, yeah, crash it right down on your car.___ I don't know

© Copyright 1997 PolyGram Music Publishing Limited, 47 British Grove, London W4.
All Rights Reserved. International Copyright Secured.

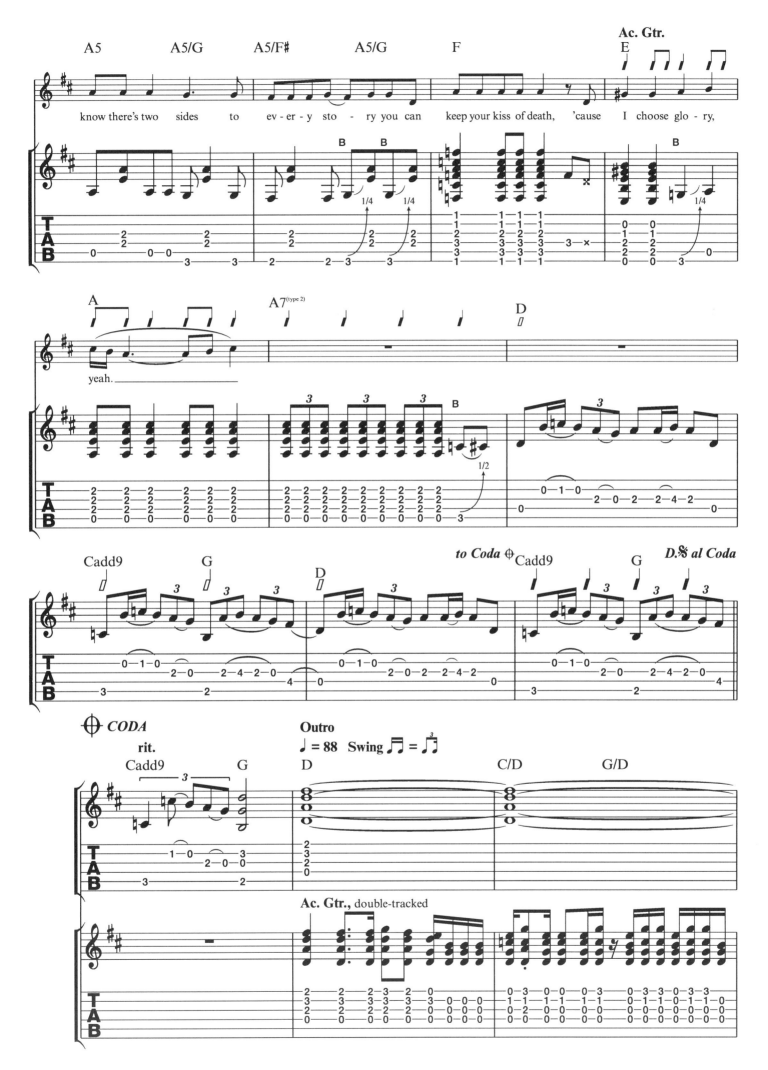

know there's two sides to ev‑er‑y sto ‑ ry you can keep your kiss of death, 'cause I choose glo ‑ ry,

yeah.

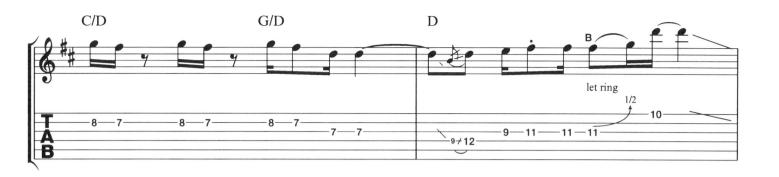
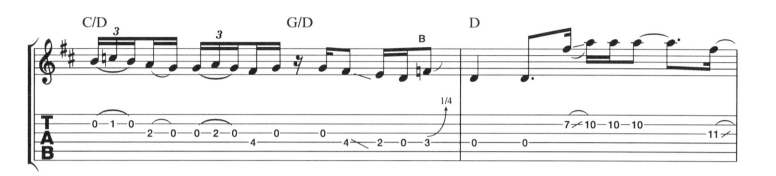
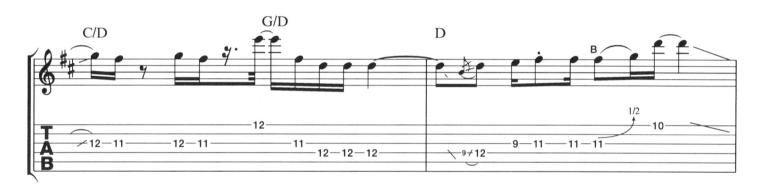
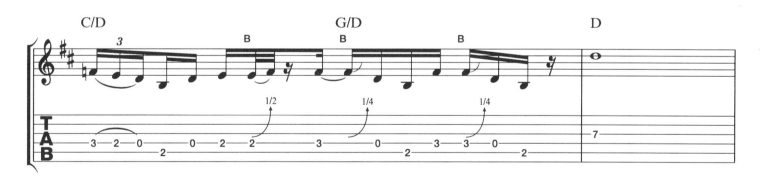
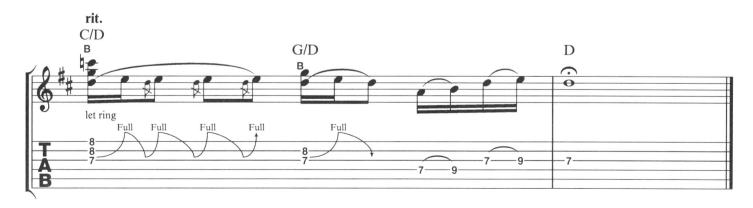

LOVE ME AND LEAVE ME

Words & Music by John Squire & Liam Gallagher

© Copyright 1997 PolyGram Music Publishing Limited, 47 British Grove, London W4 (50%) & Sony/ATV Music Publishing, 10 Great Marlborough Street, London W1 (50%).
All Rights Reserved. International Copyright Secured.

Chorus

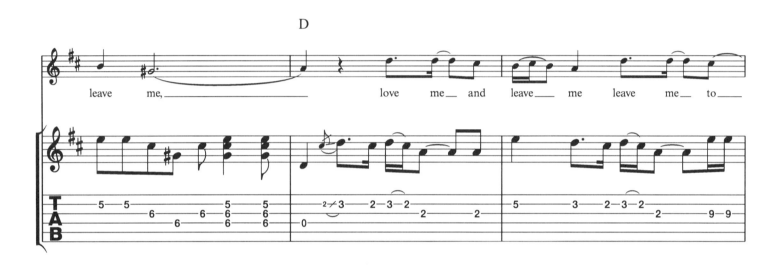

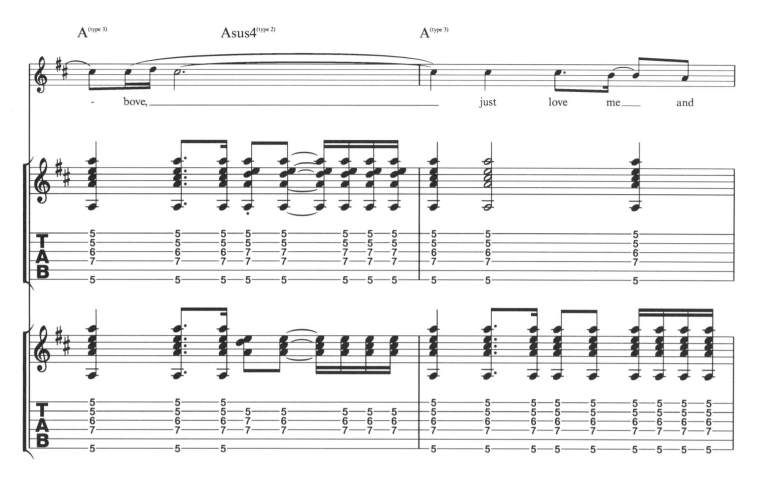

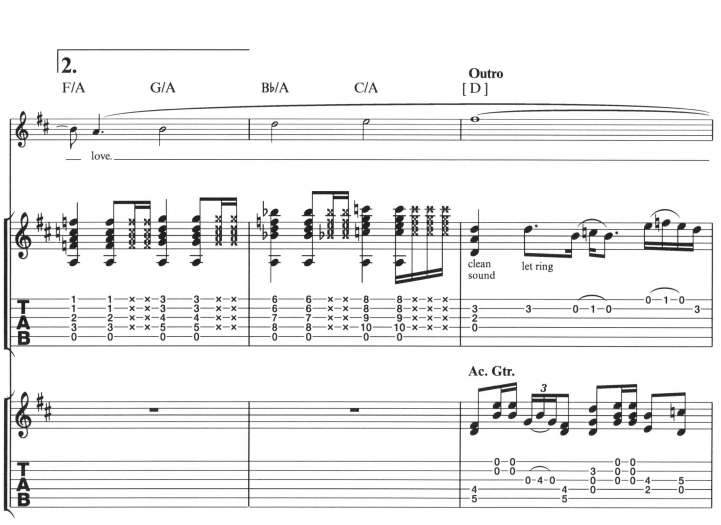

fade

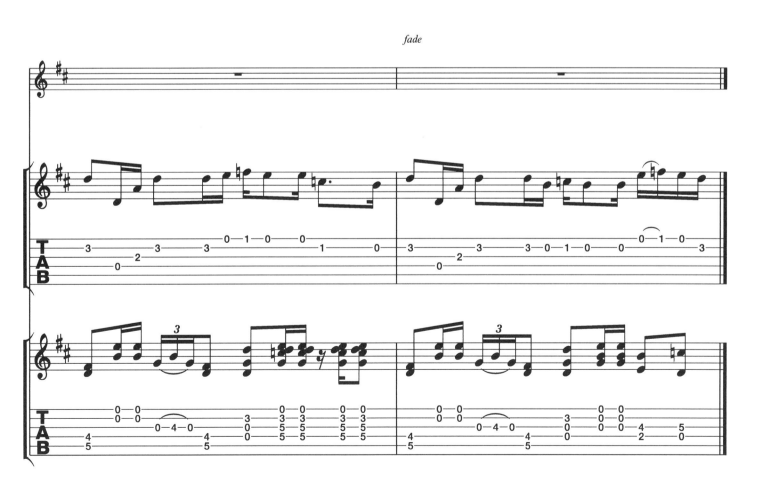

ROUND THE UNIVERSE

Words & Music by John Squire

Rhythm guitars Capo 2

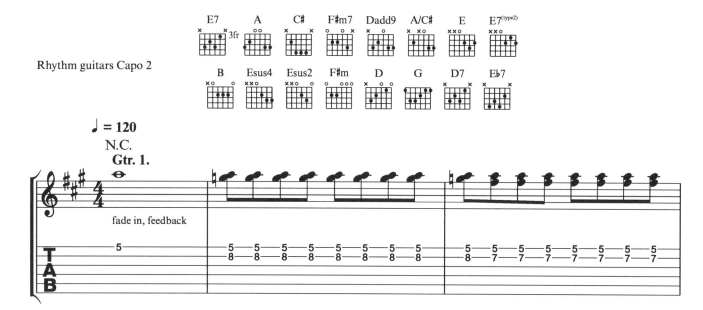

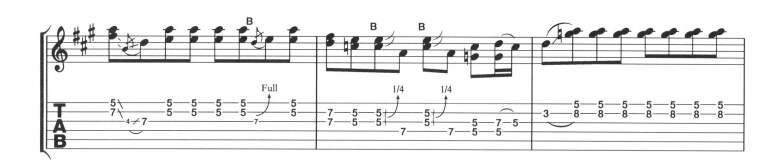

rit.

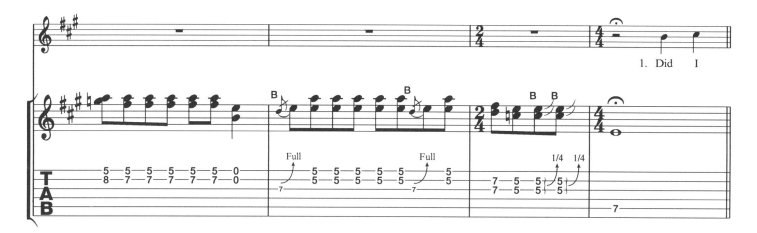

© Copyright 1997 PolyGram Music Publishing Limited, 47 British Grove, London W4.
All Rights Reserved. International Copyright Secured.

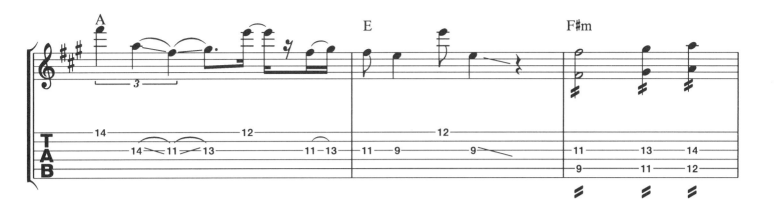

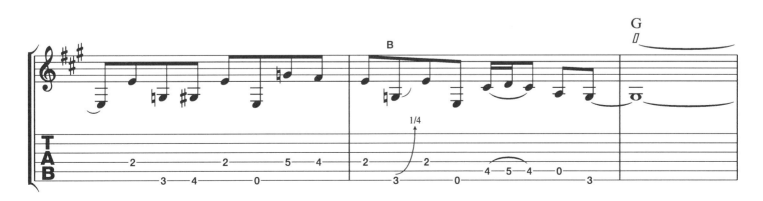

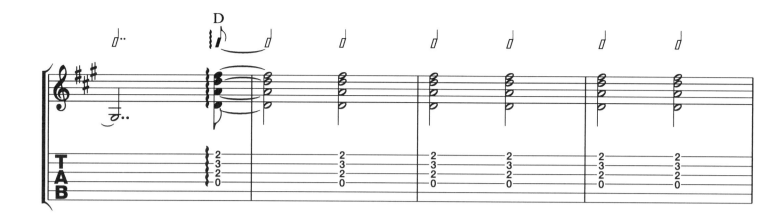

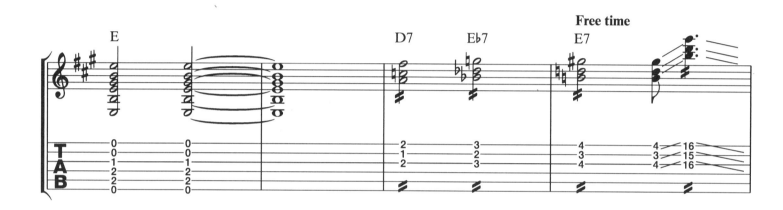

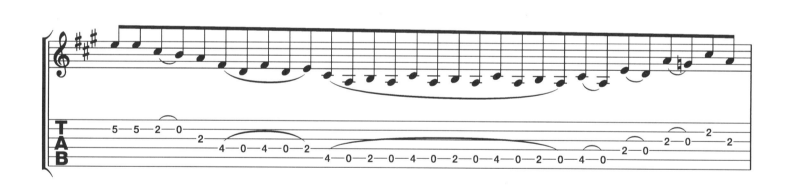

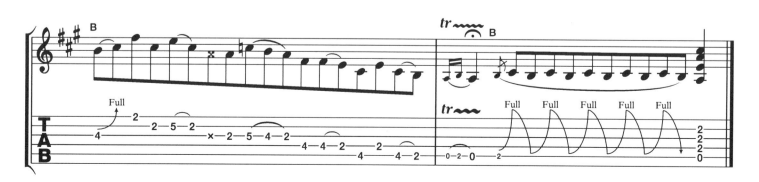

1999

Words & Music by John Squire

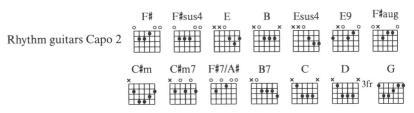

Rhythm guitars Capo 2

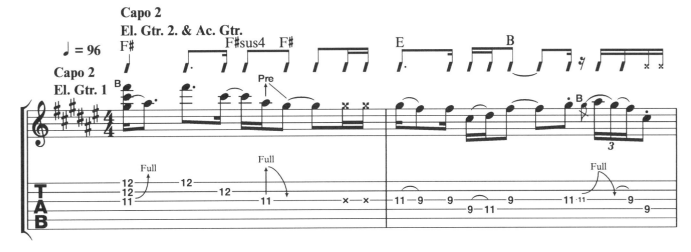

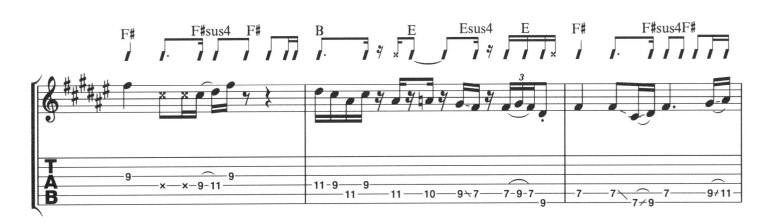

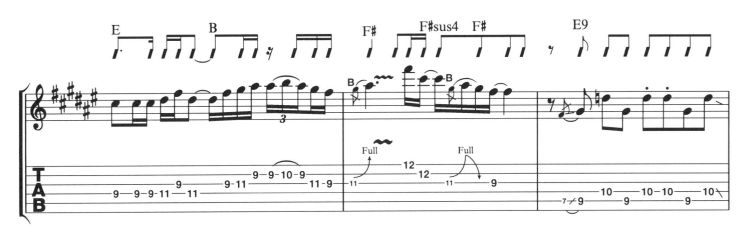

© Copyright 1997 PolyGram Music Publishing Limited, 47 British Grove, London W4.
All Rights Reserved. International Copyright Secured.

STANDING ON YOUR HEAD

Words & Music by John Squire

Tune DADGAD, Capo 2

♩ = 66

Tune 6th string to D,
2nd string to A,
1st string to D, Capo 2

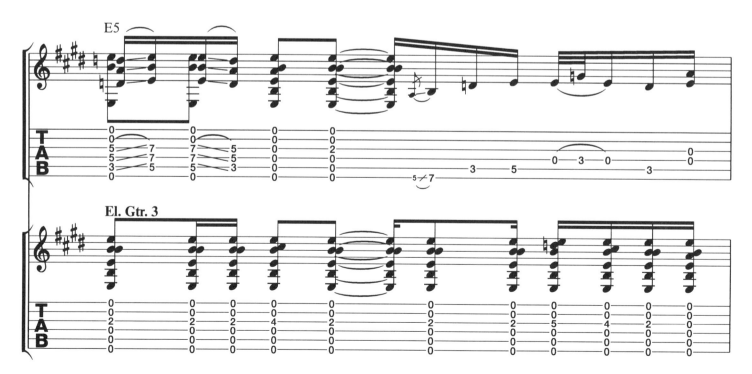

© Copyright 1997 PolyGram Music Publishing Limited, 47 British Grove, London W4.
All Rights Reserved. International Copyright Secured.

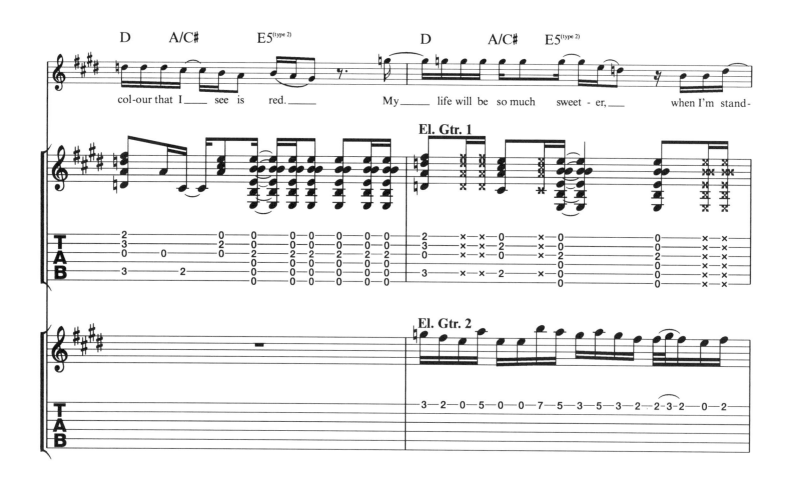

col-our that I___ see is red.___   My___ life will be so much   sweet - er,___   when I'm stand-

to Coda ⊕

- ing   tall___   on your   head.___

Verse 3

And when you reach the bottom when you hit my killing floor
I'll be there to greet you and show you to the door
It's a bright sunny day, not a cloud in the sky
So say your prayers one last time

HELLO

Words & Music by Chris Helme

© Copyright 1997 PolyGram Music Publishing Limited, 47 British Grove, London W4.
All Rights Reserved. International Copyright Secured.

Exclusive Distributors:
Music Sales Limited, 8/9 Frith Street, London W1V 5TZ, England.
Music Sales Pty Limited, 120 Rothschild Avenue, Rosebery, NSW 2018, Australia.

Order No. AM950554
ISBN 0-7119-7033-5

This book © Copyright 1997 by Wise Publications.

Visit the Internet Music Shop at http://www.musicsales.co.uk

Unauthorised reproduction of any part of this publication by any means including photocopying is an infringement of copyright.

Music arranged and processed by Barnes Music Engraving.

Printed in the United Kingdom by Staples Printers Limited, Rochester, Kent.

Your Guarantee of Quality:
As publishers, we strive to produce every book to the highest commercial standards.
The music has been freshly engraved and, whilst endeavouring to retain the original running order of the recorded album,
the book has been carefully designed to minimise awkward page turns and to make playing from it a real pleasure.
Particular care has been given to specifying acid-free, neutral-sized paper made from pulps which have not been elemental chlorine bleached.
This pulp is from farmed sustainable forests and was produced with special regard for the environment.
Throughout, the printing and binding have been planned to ensure a sturdy, attractive publication which should give years of enjoyment.
If your copy fails to meet our high standards, please inform us and we will gladly replace it.

Music Sales' complete catalogue describes thousands of titles and is available in full colour sections by subject, direct from Music Sales Limited.
Please state your areas of interest and send a cheque/postal order for £1.50 for postage to:
Music Sales Limited, Newmarket Road, Bury St. Edmunds, Suffolk IP33 3YB.